DISCOVER SHAPES

Françoise Audry-Iljic and Thierry Courtin
Adapted by Judith Herbst

BARRON'S

First English language edition published in 1995 by
Barron's Educational Series, Inc. English translation/adaptation
© Copyright 1995 by Barron's Educational Series, Inc.

Address all inquiries to:
Barron's Educational Series, Inc.
250 Wireless Boulevard
Hauppauge, New York 11788

Library of Congress Catalog Card No. 94-37327

International Standard Book No. 0-8120-6499-2

Library of Congress Cataloging-in-Publication Data
Herbst, Judith
    Discover shapes / Françoise Audry-Iljic and Thierry Courtin ;
adapted by Judith Herbst.
        p. cm.
    ISBN 0-8120-6499-2
    1. Geometry—Juvenile literature.   I. Audry-Iljic, Françoise.
Découverte des formes. II. Courtin, Thierry. III. Title.
QA445.5.H47   1995
516'.15—dc20   94-37327
                                                                                    CIP

Printed in France
5678 9655 987654321

THE STORY OF SHAPES

All children love to draw, cut, glue, and play with construction paper. And it's not by chance that marbles, balls, balloons, cubes, blocks, and cardboard tubes are as enticing to them as a ball of wool is to a kitten. As budding artists and builders, they are on their way to discovering shapes, an essential step in their development.

Very early on, children can tell the difference between straight and bent, round and pointed, open and closed, flat and raised. But the big step is learning to recognize and identify a shape as simple as a triangle, whether it is hidden among other shapes, whatever its color or make-up, or if its size and proportions have changed.

Simple shapes are merely geometric inventions of which there are few perfect examples in the world. But for us, they serve as an alphabet that allows us to analyze and understand all existing forms, to copy them and to create new ones.

This book will help your child journey through the exploration of the most basic shapes: from point to line, from closed line to open line, from area to volume. In each drawing, the shape in question is presented in a realistic setting. And if your child makes a game out of every page, that's because, at this age, learning is playing and playing is learning.

And so, your child will enter a world of imagination and creativity in which the only rule is to do and undo and redo again, to build only to tear down and to rebuild better, all with the greatest pleasure.

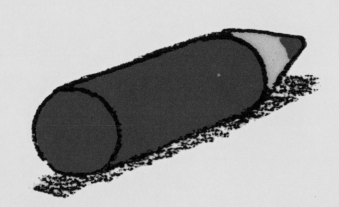

A **point** is very, very small,
It's hardly even there at all;
But every mark and every line
And every drawing and design
Begins with just a pencil dot;
A point's the perfect starting spot.

Big star, bright star,
Oh how far away you are;
Twinkling in the summer night,
Looking like a point of light.

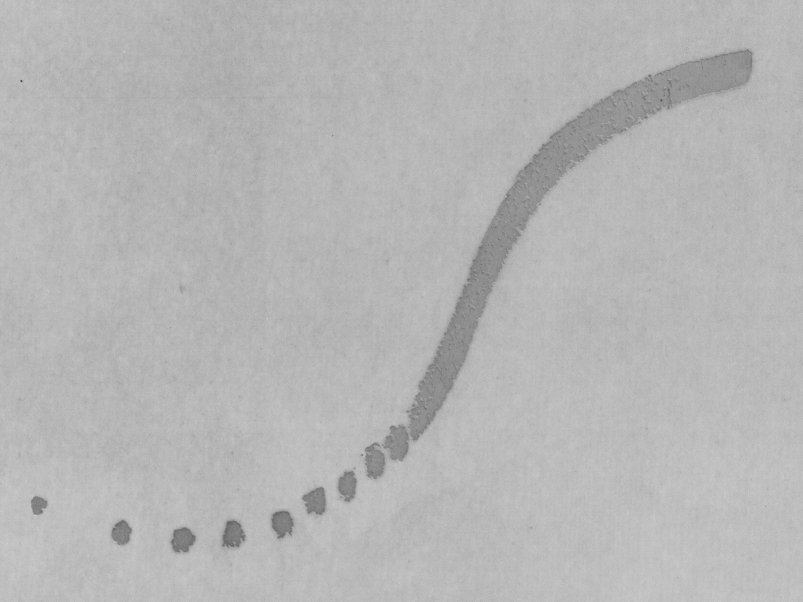

One point, two points, three points, four,
Close together on the floor;
Five points, six points, let's add more;
Teeny, tiny points galore.

Little points like little ants,
Marching past my garden plants;
Points that form a long, long row;
Soon a **line** begins to grow.

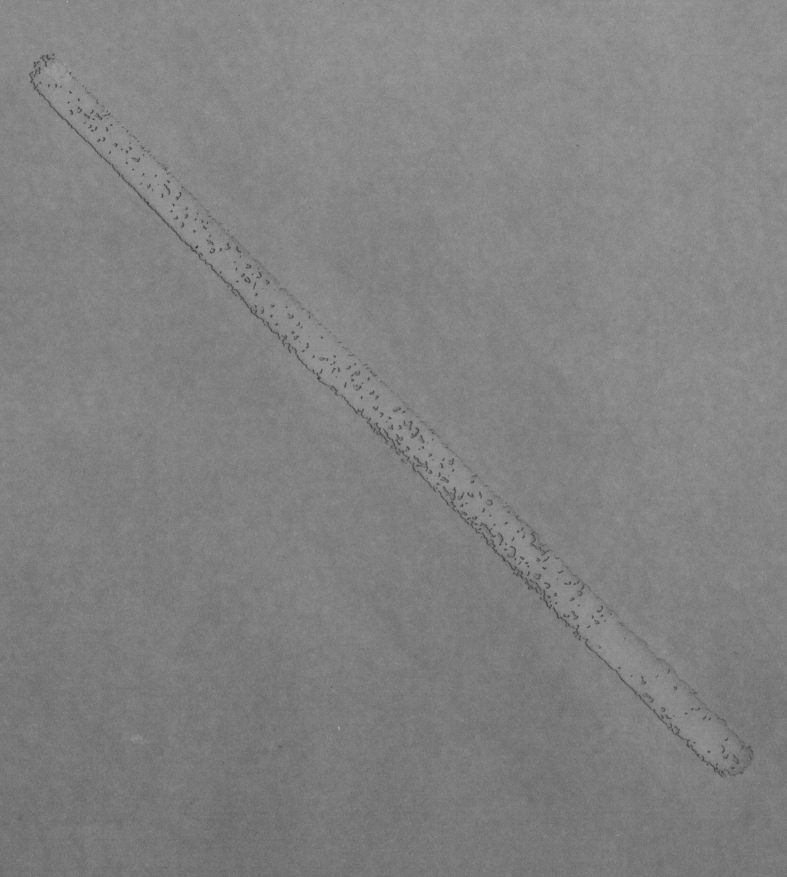

Now, here's a line that has no bumps,
No crinkles, wrinkles, folds, or lumps;
It doesn't turn and doesn't bend,
It's flat and smooth from end to end.

I know you've seen this line before,
It's like the rope in tug-of-war;
It's stiff and straight as you can see,
And called a **straight line**, naturally!

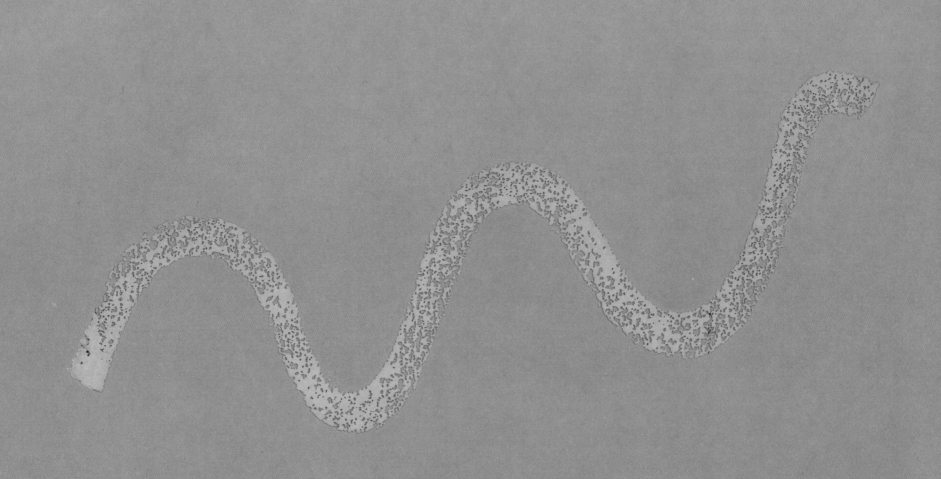

Here's a line with lots of motion,
Like a wave upon the ocean,
Like a roller coaster track,
Like a camel's bumpy back.

Wavy line, you're always bending,
Turning up and then descending,
Like a slinky sliding snake;
Oh! What pictures you will make!

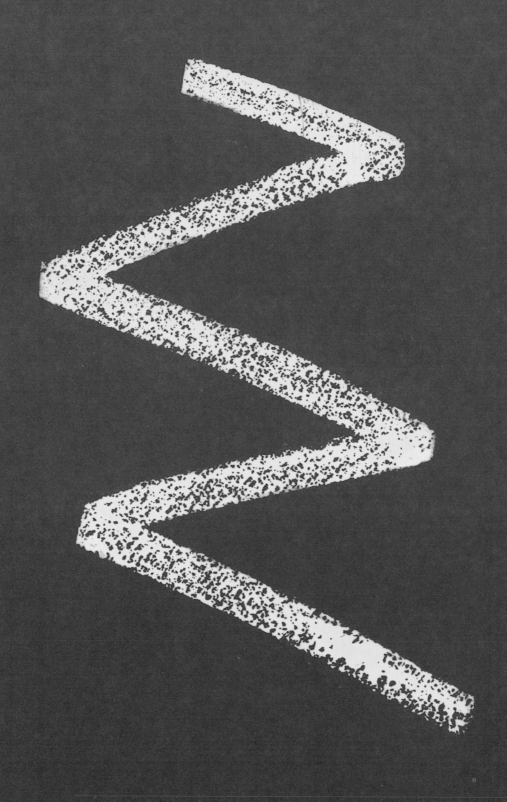

One slash here, one slash there,
Back and forth like lightning;
That's a zigzag **broken line**,
Furious and frightening.

Zip, zip, zip, right, left, right,
Makes the Z of Zorro;
Dressed in black, he'll leave his mark
And then be gone tomorrow.

A **curl** is a line that can never be straight,
Around and around it must bend;
Looping long loops that its movements create,
Trying to find its own end.

Swooping and looping, the airplane climbs high,
Leaving long curls as it turns in the sky;
Winter winds blowing will chase them away;
Skywriting pictures were not meant to stay.

What kind of shape is the **spiral**?
A curious one to be sure;
It winds itself up very tightly
Until it is feeling secure.

A hose can be wound in a spiral,
And unwound as easy as pie;
But snails must forever be spirals,
They're not made of rubber, that's why!

A **circle**, I've found, is perfectly round,
And yet, it is easy to make;
The very first thing is to tie up a string
To chalk and a small wooden stake.

Then round goes the chalk on its circular walk
And there in the ground at your feet,
The chalk line will bend till it finds its own end
And your circle is full and complete.

Dots and zigzags, lines and spirals,
Curls and curlicues,

Look at all the dandy shapes
There are for you to use.

A circle keeps everything in,
It doesn't quite end or begin;
It makes a round space
That's a flattened-out place,
A **disk** that's exceedingly thin.

A disk is a pancake you flip in the air,
It never gets dizzy cause pancakes don't care;
A disk can turn over and still look the same,
So let's all have pancakes and call them by name.

An **oval** is a circle
That is not exactly round,
It seems a little stretched out,
Like a light spot on the ground.

If you can draw an oval,
You should save it just in case;
An oval is the perfect shape
To frame a smiling face.

The **square**'s a little block of strength
With four straight lines of equal length;
The corners that are formed inside
Are spots where lots of dust can hide.

Some people say that they have seen
A square become a trampoline.
I think that's keen!

Two long sides that face each other,
Two short sides that do the same;
Pointy corners: one, two, three, four—
Do you know its name?

A **rectangle** sometimes looks narrow and long,
And sometimes it's short but it's wide;
It simply depends on the way that it's turned,
And which is the uppermost side.

The sides of a **triangle**, as you can see,
Form sharp, pointy corners and add up to three;
If you have a square—a bandanna will do—
A fold end to end makes a triangle, too.

And should you set out for a long ocean trip,
Just hoist up a triangle sail for your ship!

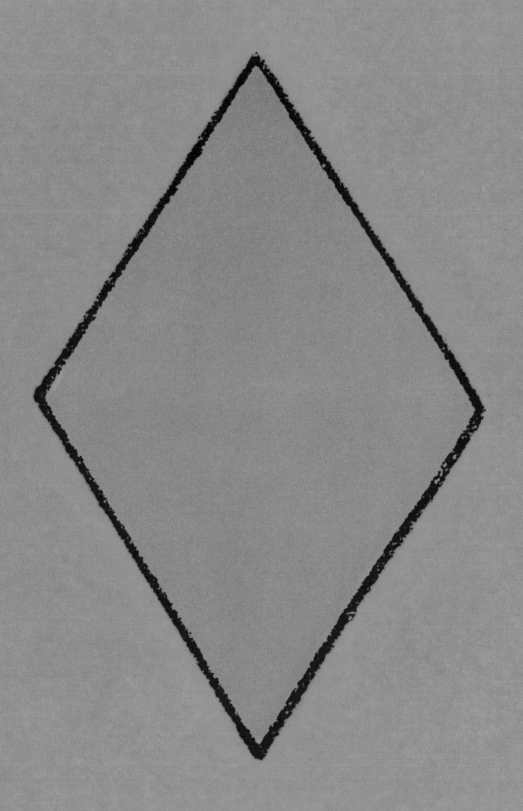

I'd know a **diamond** anywhere,
It looks just like a stretched out square;
And when it's tilted to the side,
A diamond can be long or wide.

A bunch of diamonds could combine
To make a suit that's really fine;
And if I had an extra one,
I'd build a kite when I was done.

Some circles, some squares, and some triangles, too;
Oh, what can you do with a scissors and glue?

Mix them and match them, and paste them and patch them,
And let your ideas and creations shine through!

Behold the simple **cylinder**,
It's such a nifty shape;
Just roll a piece of paper up
And fasten it with tape.

But if it's hollow through and through,
And something you can see into—
A drinking straw, a place to crawl—
It's called a **tube** by one and all.

Oh **roller**, steam roller, you flatten and crush,
Smoothing the tar, turning pebbles to mush.
Steam rolling cylinder, solid and thick,
Closed at both ends like a log or a stick.

Paint rollers, rolling pins rolling out pies,
You can find rollers in just the right size.

Little bubble, little **sphere**,
All too soon you disappear;
Making rainbows in the light,
Till you rise and pop from sight.

Beach balls, and baseballs, and big balls galore,
Marbles, and small balls, and so many more,
Round rolling spheres all spread out on the floor.

An egg is a wobbily mover,
Its two ends are not the same size;
But eggs hold a treasure
No ruler can measure,

What pops out is such a surprise!

A **cube** is a shape with a lot of pizzazz,
Just look at the fabulous features it has:
A cube doesn't wobble or roll anywhere,
Its six flattened sides are all perfectly square.

Just stack them together by two and by four,
And lo and behold! You can keep building more.

My lovely assistant, a brave volunteer,
Fits into this box without worry or fear;
It's not like a cube that will squish her too tight,
Cause three sides are longer and just the right height.

The very same shape, if it's solid and thick,
And smaller in size can turn into a brick;
Then stack them and set them so they'll never fall,
And brick by brick, magically, you'll make a wall.

I'd much rather sleep in a tent;
Away from the street lights, the cars, and cement;
A **pyramid** tent with a floor that is square,

So I could stretch out in the cool forest air,
Or maybe a tent in the shape of a **cone**,
Then I'd have a hideaway all of my own.

Well, my oh my, imagine that!
A cone can be a spiffy hat;

But turn it around and you've got something new—
A holder for ice cream! Now, one scoop or two?

Cones and rollers, blocks and cubes,
Cylinders, and narrow tubes...

Space them, place them, stack them tall,
Soon you will have built a wall.
Crayons, paper, sticky tape.
Wow! Your castle's taking shape!

Oh no! Look out! A wrecking ball! A smashing, crashing mess!
A falling over free-for-all, but I'll rebuild it, yes!

And one by one the walls will rise upon my playroom floor,
Until my castle's twice the size than what it was before.